War at Sea 1337-1340
By David Nicolle

Edward III, c. 1340

In 1340, Edward the English king assumed the title of ruler over France and had his golden leopards on a red ground quartered with France's golden lilies on a blue ground. He holds a shield bearing his new arms, although his surcoat still only shows the Plantagenet leopards. Sources: Effigies of Jn. of Eltham and Jn. Leverick, c. 1340, Westminster Abbey and Ash, Kent; stone canopy of the Percy tomb, c. 1342-45, Beverly Church, England.

Bellerophon Books

English Lady, c. 1340

The 100 Years War started off as a feudal conflict which everyone expected to be full of chivalrous feats. Many English ladies watched the battle of Sluys in June, 1340, some being killed in a crossfire. Sources: brasses of Lady de Northwood, wives of R. Brauche and Sir J. de Creke, c. 1330, 1364 and 1325, Minster Church, Sheppey; St. Margaret's, Lynn, Norfolk; Westley Waterless, Cambridgeshire.

Bellerophon Books

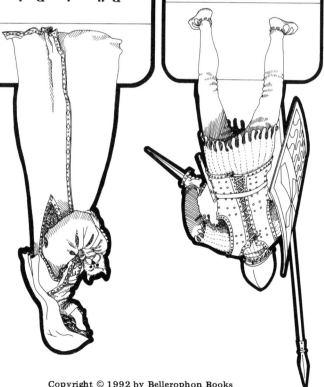

Genoese Marine, c. 1340

Italians and Spaniards were by far the most experienced naval warriors of the 14th century, and their warships were in great demand. Genoese galleys fought for both England and France. Sources: Frescoes, c. 1340, Castle of Sabbionara, Avio, Italy; fresco by Simone Martini, c. 1335, Church of San Francesco, Assisi; 'Law,' MS Royal E IX, British Library.

Bellerophon Books

French Knight arming c. 1345

French knights had more up-to-date equipment than the English. This French knight is donning a coat-of-plates in which the iron sheets are riveted inside a decorative leather covering. Sources: Coat-of-plates from Wisby, c. 1360, National Museum, Stockholm; brass of De Heere family, 1332, Brussels; hauberk, 14th century, Royal Scottish Museum, Edinburgh.

Bellerophon Books

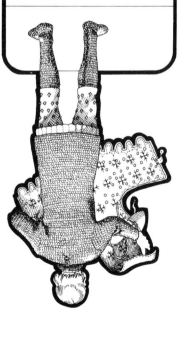

Campaigns of Cambrai, Tournai, War of Succession in Brittany 1339-1343

German Knight, c. 1340

Germany, or the Holy Roman Empire, provided numbers of mercenaries, many of whom fought for Edward of England during the early stages of the war. German armour also had some characteristic features, including a moveable visor attached to the mail coif, but linked to the helmet only by a turn-buckle. German fashions often also seemed more decorative than those of their western neighbors. Sources: Effigies of Albrecht von Hohenlohe, Otto von Orlamunde, c. 1340, Schonthal an der Jagst and Himmelkron, Germany; and Ulrich de Werd, c. 1345, St. William's Church, Strasbourg, France.

Bellerophon Books

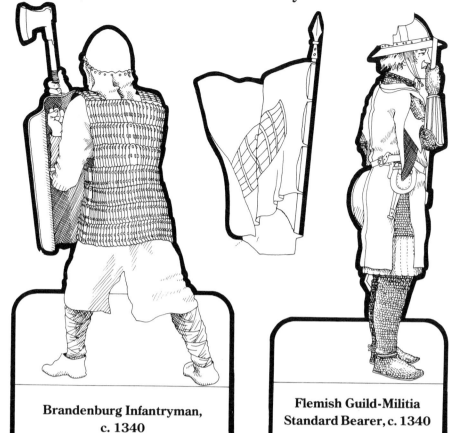

Brandenburg Infantryman, c. 1340

The Elector of Brandenburg, Lewis V, was one of Edward of England's allies. Although this alliance was short-lived, a Brandenburg contingent plundered northern France in 1339. Brandenburg lay on the frontier of the German and Slav worlds. This warrior is from the latter tradition, as is shown by his lamellar armour and curiously shaped shield. Sources: Mazovian seals, 1341-1387, National Museum, Warsaw; German bascinet helmet, mid-14th century, Cracow Cathedral; St. George from Novgorod, early 14th century, Russkaya Museum, Moscow.

Bellerophon Books

Flemish Guild-Militia Standard Bearer, c. 1340

Infantry from the Low Countries were caught up in the 100 Years War. Militias of the towns of present day Belgium had long been famous as defensive warriors fighting with pikes and falchion-type swords (as shown here). Sources: Statues of Ghent levies from the Belfry, c. 1340, Stonework Museum, Ghent; frieze of 'Sleeping Guards,' Freiburg im Breisgau, Germany.

Bellerophon Books

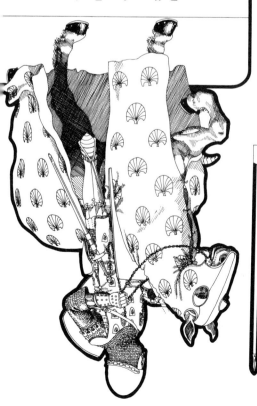

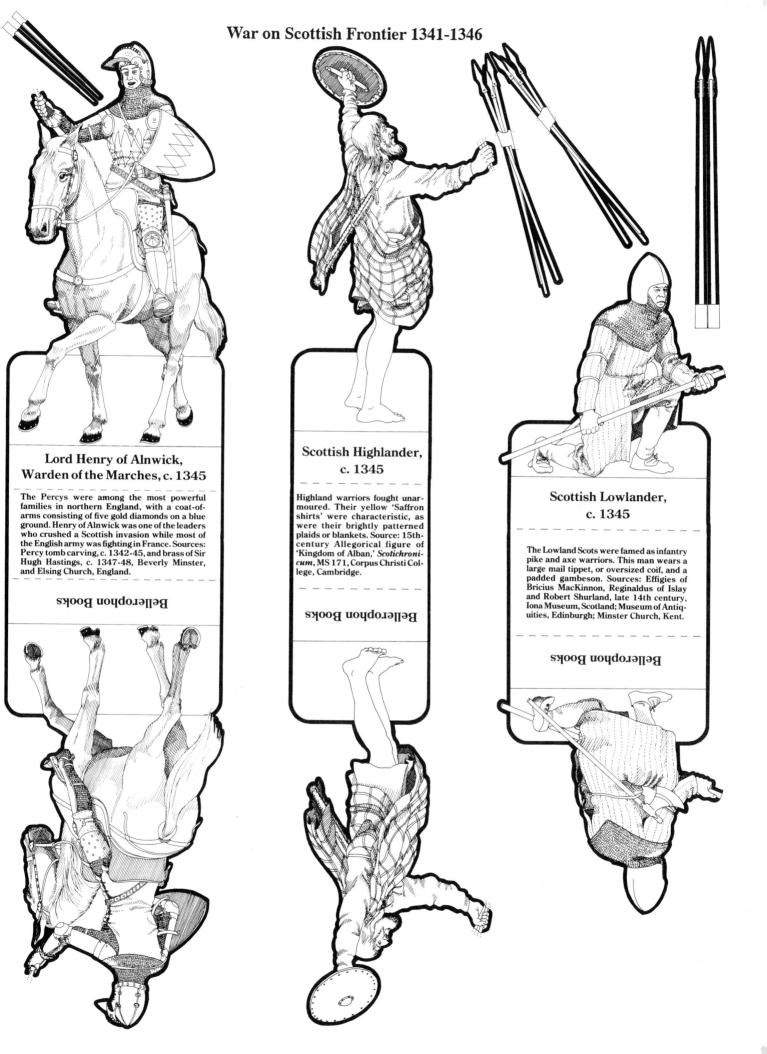

Lord Henry of Alnwick, Warden of the Marches, c. 1345

The Percys were among the most powerful families in northern England, with a coat-of-arms consisting of five gold diamonds on a blue ground. Henry of Alnwick was one of the leaders who crushed a Scottish invasion while most of the English army was fighting in France. Sources: Percy tomb carving, c. 1342-45, and brass of Sir Hugh Hastings, c. 1347-48, Beverly Minster, and Elsing Church, England.

Bellerophon Books

Scottish Highlander, c. 1345

Highland warriors fought unarmoured. Their yellow 'Saffron shirts' were characteristic, as were their brightly patterned plaids or blankets. Source: 15th-century Allegorical figure of 'Kingdom of Alban,' *Scotichronicum*, MS 171, Corpus Christi College, Cambridge.

Bellerophon Books

Scottish Lowlander, c. 1345

The Lowland Scots were famed as infantry pike and axe warriors. This man wears a large mail tippet, or oversized coif, and a padded gambeson. Sources: Effigies of Bricius MacKinnon, Reginaldus of Islay and Robert Shurland, late 14th century, Iona Museum, Scotland; Museum of Antiquities, Edinburgh; Minster Church, Kent.

Bellerophon Books

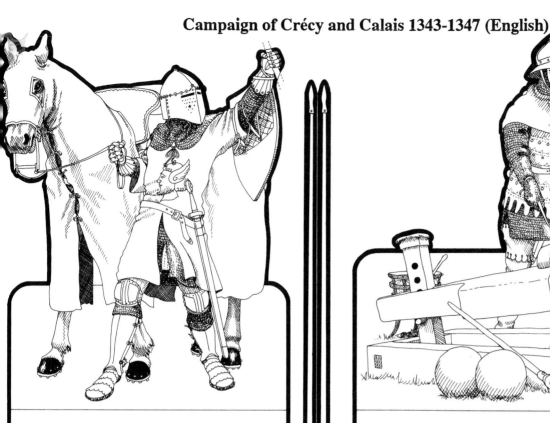

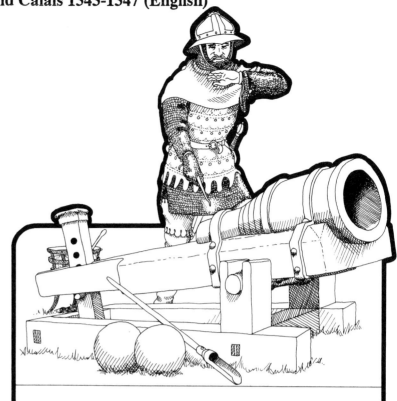

John de Grailly, Captal
de Buch, c. 1350

The Captal de Buch was one of the most powerful men in the Plantagenet province of Gascony. He was also a fine soldier, being partly responsible for the great Anglo-Gascon victory at Poitiers. His coat-of-arms was a Midas Head, a human head with ass's ears, although its colours are not recorded. Sources: Mid-14th century frescoes and helmet from Templer Chapel, St. Floret castle, France, and Kussnacht castle, Schweizerisches Landesmuseum, Zurich.

Flemish Gunner with Bombard,
c. 1345

Many of Europe's first artillerymen and gun-founders came from Flanders. They served in many armies and one of their most effective weapons was the bombard. Although mainly for siege warfare, bombards were sometimes used in open battle to frighten the enemy's horses. Sources: 'Romance of Alexander,' Flemish manuscript, c. 1340, MS 264, Bodleian Lib; Italian bombard, 14th century, Artillery Museum, Turin; 'Guards at Tomb,' carving, c. 1345, Musée de l'Oeuvre Notre-Dame, Strasbourg; 'Antiquities Flandriae,' Flemish manuscript, 1342, MS 13076-77, Bib. Royale, Brussels.

Bellerophon Books

Bellerophon Books

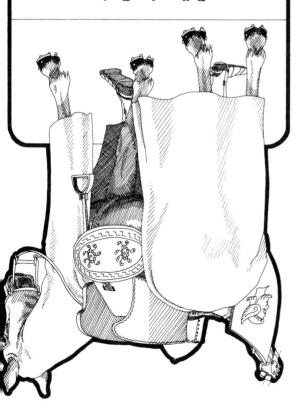

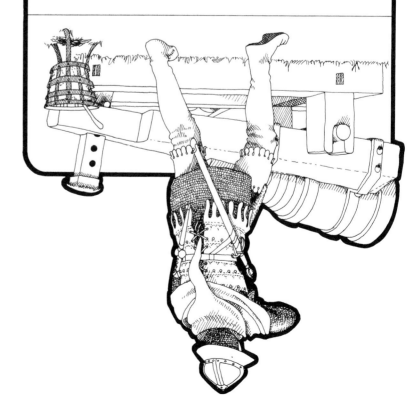

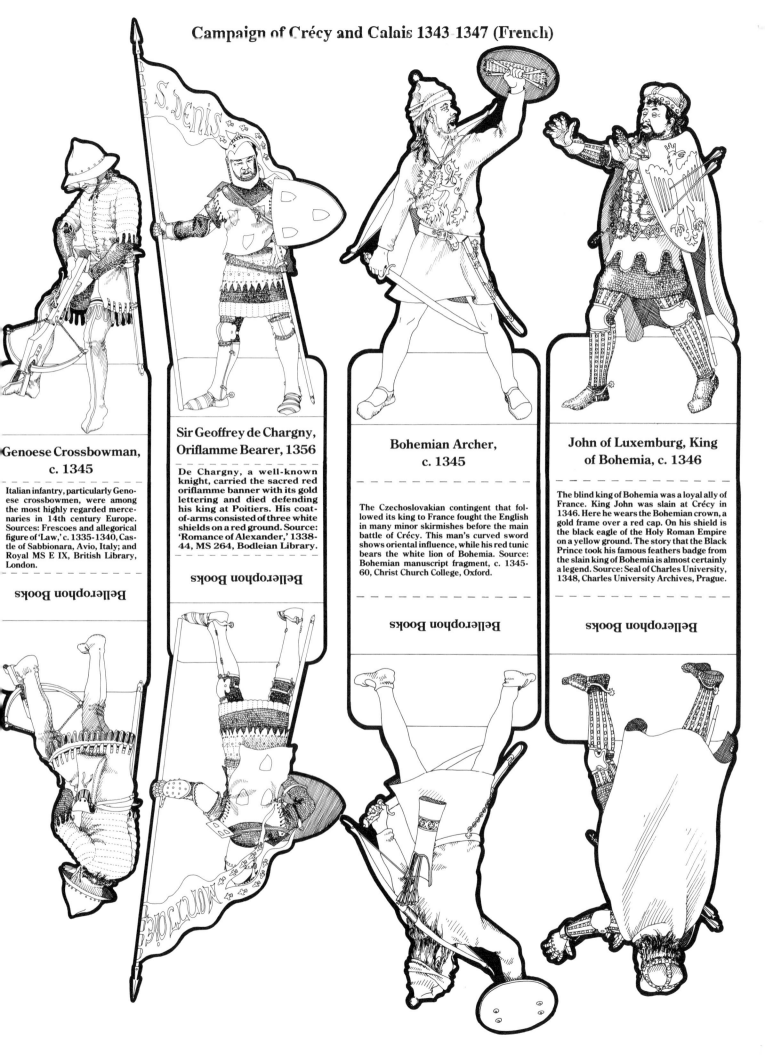

Genoese Crossbowman, c. 1345

Italian infantry, particularly Genoese crossbowmen, were among the most highly regarded mercenaries in 14th century Europe. Sources: Frescoes and allegorical figure of 'Law,' c. 1335-1340, Castle of Sabbionara, Avio, Italy; and Royal MS E IX, British Library, London.

Bellerophon Books

Sir Geoffrey de Chargny, Oriflamme Bearer, 1356

De Chargny, a well-known knight, carried the sacred red oriflamme banner with its gold lettering and died defending his king at Poitiers. His coat-of-arms consisted of three white shields on a red ground. Source: 'Romance of Alexander,' 1338-44, MS 264, Bodleian Library.

Bellerophon Books

Bohemian Archer, c. 1345

The Czechoslovakian contingent that followed its king to France fought the English in many minor skirmishes before the main battle of Crécy. This man's curved sword shows oriental influence, while his red tunic bears the white lion of Bohemia. Source: Bohemian manuscript fragment, c. 1345-60, Christ Church College, Oxford.

Bellerophon Books

John of Luxemburg, King of Bohemia, c. 1346

The blind king of Bohemia was a loyal ally of France. King John was slain at Crécy in 1346. Here he wears the Bohemian crown, a gold frame over a red cap. On his shield is the black eagle of the Holy Roman Empire on a yellow ground. The story that the Black Prince took his famous feathers badge from the slain king of Bohemia is almost certainly a legend. Source: Seal of Charles University, 1348, Charles University Archives, Prague.

Bellerophon Books

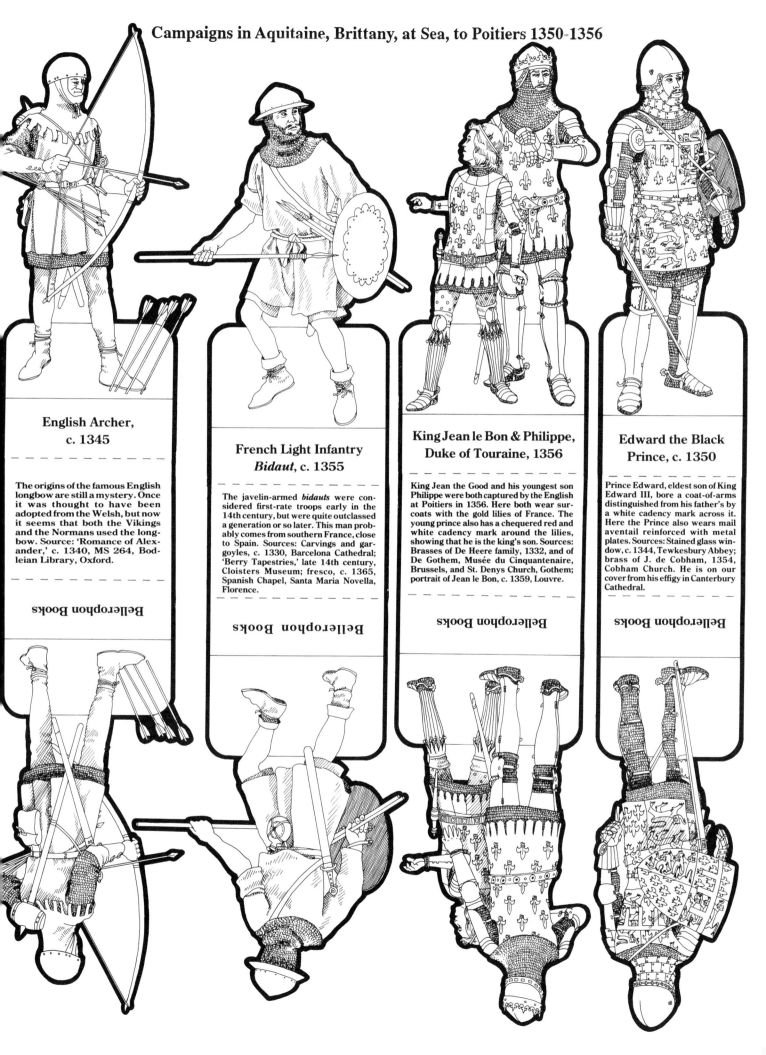

English Archer, c. 1345

The origins of the famous English longbow are still a mystery. Once it was thought to have been adopted from the Welsh, but now it seems that both the Vikings and the Normans used the longbow. Source: 'Romance of Alexander,' c. 1340, MS 264, Bodleian Library, Oxford.

Bellerophon Books

French Light Infantry *Bidaut*, c. 1355

The javelin-armed *bidauts* were considered first-rate troops early in the 14th century, but were quite outclassed a generation or so later. This man probably comes from southern France, close to Spain. Sources: Carvings and gargoyles, c. 1330, Barcelona Cathedral; 'Berry Tapestries,' late 14th century, Cloisters Museum; fresco, c. 1365, Spanish Chapel, Santa Maria Novella, Florence.

Bellerophon Books

King Jean le Bon & Philippe, Duke of Touraine, 1356

King Jean the Good and his youngest son Philippe were both captured by the English at Poitiers in 1356. Here both wear surcoats with the gold lilies of France. The young prince also has a chequered red and white cadency mark around the lilies, showing that he is the king's son. Sources: Brasses of De Heere family, 1332, and of De Gothem, Musée du Cinquantenaire, Brussels, and St. Denys Church, Gothem; portrait of Jean le Bon, c. 1359, Louvre.

Bellerophon Books

Edward the Black Prince, c. 1350

Prince Edward, eldest son of King Edward III, bore a coat-of-arms distinguished from his father's by a white cadency mark across it. Here the Prince also wears mail aventail reinforced with metal plates. Sources: Stained glass window, c. 1344, Tewkesbury Abbey; brass of J. de Cobham, 1354, Cobham Church. He is on our cover from his effigy in Canterbury Cathedral.

Bellerophon Books

Revolt of Jacquerie 1358

Aristocratic French Lady, c. 1358

This lady wears the height of fashion, including a new Italian hat. Her dress shows her family arms partitioned vertically. Sources: Brass of wife of De Gothem, 1358, St. Denys Church, Gothem; brass of wife of R. Torryngton, 1356, Great Berkhampstead Church; fresco by Francesco Traini, c. 1350, Camposanto, Pisa.

Bellerophon Books

Female Flagellant, c. 1358

Processions of flagellants, men and women, were seen all over Europe, during and after the Black Death. Some turned aside to massacre the Jews while others gave their blood-stained clothes as relics to their credulous followers. Sources: 'Annales of Gilles li Muisis,' 14th century, MS 13076-77, Bib. Royale, Brussels; 'Belles Heures de Duc de Berry,' late 14th century, Cloisters Museum, New York.

Bellerophon Books

Peasant member of the Jacquerie, c. 1358

The 14th century French peasant uprising known as the Jacquerie was horrific. Owing their initial success to surprise and ferocity, the Jacques were later massacred in thousands by the professional warriors of France. Sources: 'Belles Heures of Duc de Berry,' late 14th century manuscript, Cloisters Museum; 'Roman de Fauvel,' early 14th century manuscript, MS Fr. 146, Bib. Nationale, Paris.

Bellerophon Books

Militiaman of the Paris levy, c. 1360

The urban levies of rich cities like Paris were often well equipped and effective. This man wears a war-hat, with one side painted red and the other blue, over a bascinet. His large mantlet or shield is also half red and half blue, with the arms of Paris at the center. Sources: 'Chroniques de France,' c. 1375, Bib. Nationale, Paris; stained-glass window, 14th century, Rosenwiller Church, Bas-Rhin, France.

Bellerophon Books

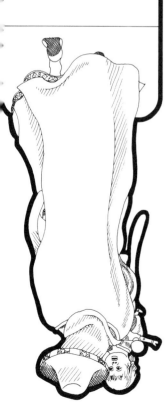
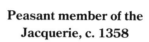
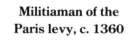
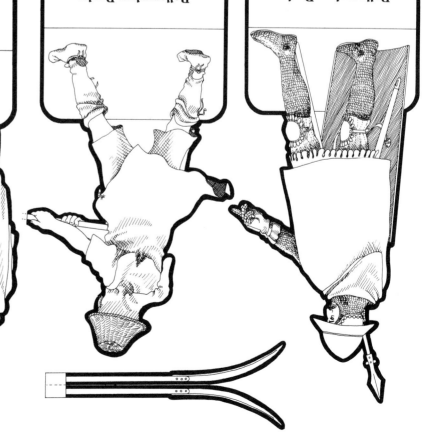

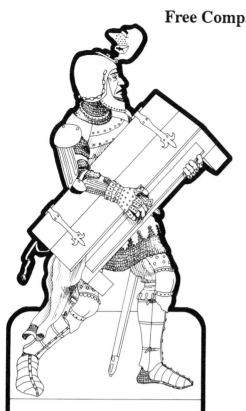

German Routier, c. 1365

The unemployed mercenaries who ravaged France after the Treaty of Brétigny were known as *routiers*. They included English, French, Bretons, Gascons, Spaniards and Germans. This man wears a coat-of-plates and a bascinet with a *klappvisier*. Sources: German helmet, wooden carving on the 'Levitic Pew,' and effigy of Duke Christopher, all mid-14th century; Tower Armouries, London; Verden Cathedral, Germany; Roskilde Cathedral, Denmark.

Bellerophon Books

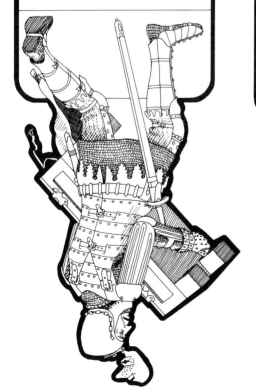

Herald of the Sire de Coucy, c. 1360

Heralds played a vital role in 14th century warfare, partly as messengers and partly as umpires to impose the rules of war. This man wears the red, white and blue arms of the Sire de Coucy, a leading French baron who spent many years as a hostage in England. Sources: Fresco, c. 1345, Papal Palace, Avignon, France; 'Annales de Gilles li Muisis,' c. 1355, MS 13076-77, Bib. Royale, Brussels.

Bellerophon Books

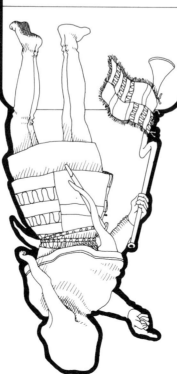

Mounted English Archer, c. 1365

Among the *routiers* who terrorized France were English archers mounted on tough ponies. This man wears a helmet of iron scales, a cloth-covered aventail and a padded gambeson. Sources: 'Chroniques de France,' late 14th century, MS Royal 20 C VII, British Library; 'Queen Mary's Psalter,' 14th century, MS Royal 10 E IV, British Library; altarpiece by Grünewald, early 16th century, Unterlinden Museum, Colmar, France.

Bellerophon Books

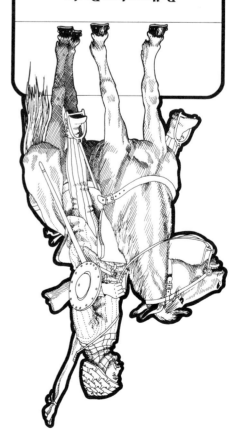

War in Castile 1365-1367

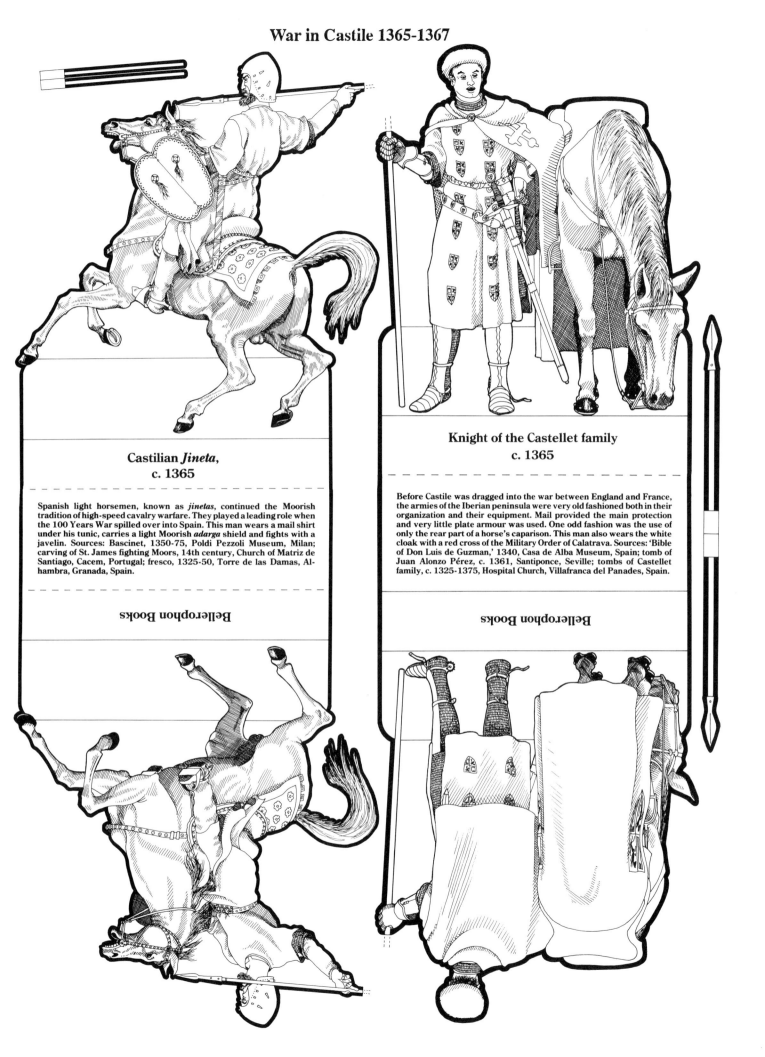

Castilian *Jineta*, c. 1365

Spanish light horsemen, known as *jinetas*, continued the Moorish tradition of high-speed cavalry warfare. They played a leading role when the 100 Years War spilled over into Spain. This man wears a mail shirt under his tunic, carries a light Moorish *adarga* shield and fights with a javelin. Sources: Bascinet, 1350-75, Poldi Pezzoli Museum, Milan; carving of St. James fighting Moors, 14th century, Church of Matriz de Santiago, Cacem, Portugal; fresco, 1325-50, Torre de las Damas, Alhambra, Granada, Spain.

Bellerophon Books

Knight of the Castellet family c. 1365

Before Castile was dragged into the war between England and France, the armies of the Iberian peninsula were very old fashioned both in their organization and their equipment. Mail provided the main protection and very little plate armour was used. One odd fashion was the use of only the rear part of a horse's caparison. This man also wears the white cloak with a red cross of the Military Order of Calatrava. Sources: 'Bible of Don Luis de Guzman,' 1340, Casa de Alba Museum, Spain; tomb of Juan Alonzo Pérez, c. 1361, Santiponce, Seville; tombs of Castellet family, c. 1325-1375, Hospital Church, Villafranca del Panades, Spain.

Bellerophon Books

Attempted Anglo-Milanese Alliance
1368

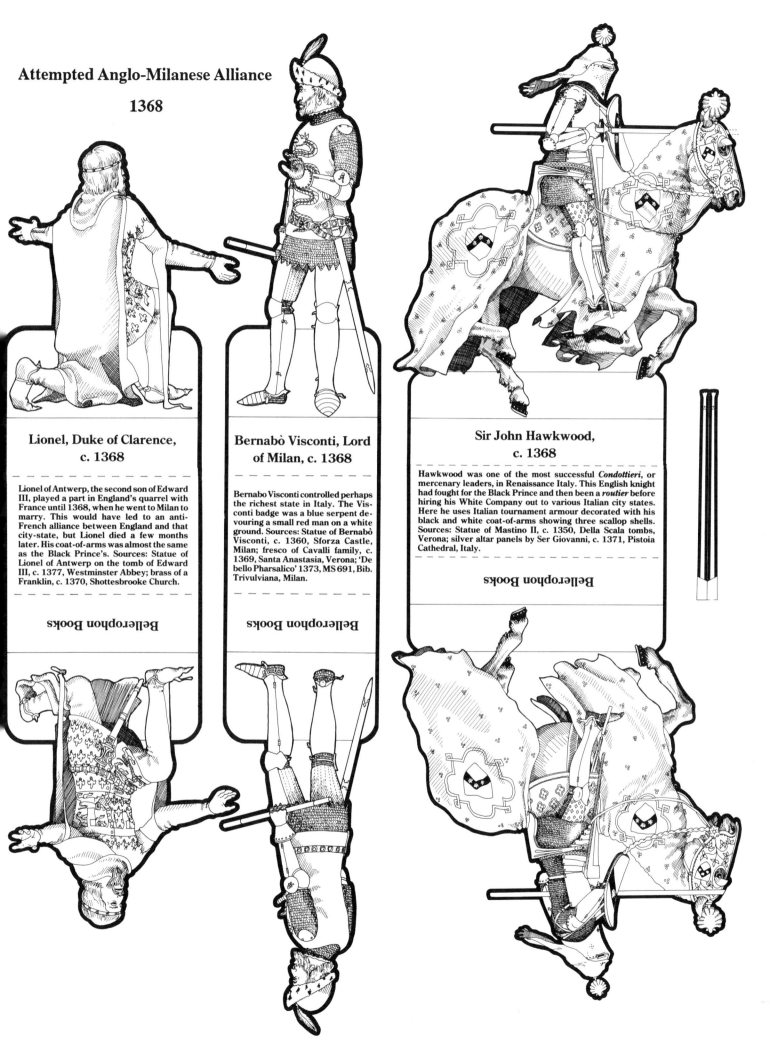

Lionel, Duke of Clarence, c. 1368

Lionel of Antwerp, the second son of Edward III, played a part in England's quarrel with France until 1368, when he went to Milan to marry. This would have led to an anti-French alliance between England and that city-state, but Lionel died a few months later. His coat-of-arms was almost the same as the Black Prince's. Sources: Statue of Lionel of Antwerp on the tomb of Edward III, c. 1377, Westminster Abbey; brass of a Franklin, c. 1370, Shottesbrooke Church.

Bellerophon Books

Bernabò Visconti, Lord of Milan, c. 1368

Bernabo Visconti controlled perhaps the richest state in Italy. The Visconti badge was a blue serpent devouring a small red man on a white ground. Sources: Statue of Bernabò Visconti, c. 1360, Sforza Castle, Milan; fresco of Cavalli family, c. 1369, Santa Anastasia, Verona; 'De bello Pharsalico' 1373, MS 691, Bib. Trivulviana, Milan.

Bellerophon Books

Sir John Hawkwood, c. 1368

Hawkwood was one of the most successful *Condottieri*, or mercenary leaders, in Renaissance Italy. This English knight had fought for the Black Prince and then been a *routier* before hiring his White Company out to various Italian city states. Here he uses Italian tournament armour decorated with his black and white coat-of-arms showing three scallop shells. Sources: Statue of Mastino II, c. 1350, Della Scala tombs, Verona; silver altar panels by Ser Giovanni, c. 1371, Pistoia Cathedral, Italy.

Bellerophon Books

Bertrand du Guesclin,
Constable of France, c. 1370

Du Guesclin, Constable of France, organized guerilla resistance against the English. His coat-of-arms was a black eagle with red beak and claws on a white ground divided by a red *cotise* or band. Sources: Ivory statuette of armoured horse, mid-14th century, British Museum; 'Du Guesclin Chronicles,' late 14th century, Bib. Nationale, Paris; 'Hystoire de Roys de France,' late 14th century, MS Royal 20 C VII, British Library, London.

Bellerophon Books

Cardinal Robert of Geneva,
c. 1375

The Papacy itself became a victim of the 100 Years War with two rival popes, one in Avignon and one in Rome, competing for international support. One of these had been the bloodthirsty Cardinal Robert of Geneva, who was elected as Clement VII in 1378. Here he wears a Cardinal's scarlet hat and cloak over a long white tunic. Sources: 'Nine Hours Tapestry,' late 14th century, Cloisters Museum; 'Grand Chroniques de France,' c. 1375, MS Fr. 2813, Bib. Nat., Paris; drawing of a mule by Pisanello, early 15th century, n. 2325, Louvre.

Bellerophon Books

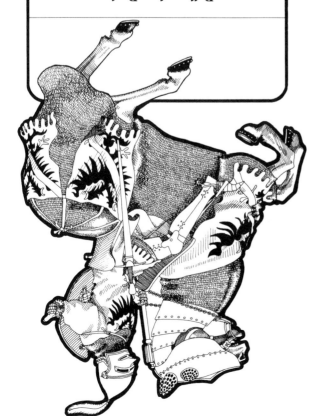

War at Sea 1372-1387

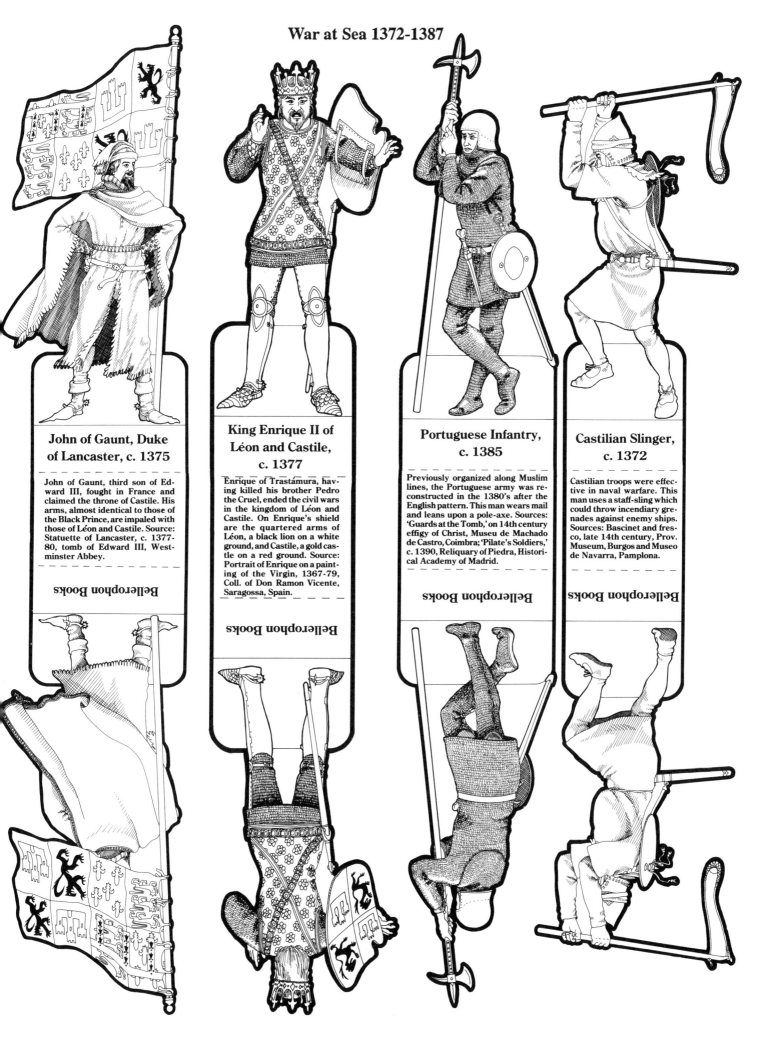

John of Gaunt, Duke of Lancaster, c. 1375

John of Gaunt, third son of Edward III, fought in France and claimed the throne of Castile. His arms, almost identical to those of the Black Prince, are impaled with those of Léon and Castile. Source: Statuette of Lancaster, c. 1377-80, tomb of Edward III, Westminster Abbey.

King Enrique II of Léon and Castile, c. 1377

Enrique of Trastámura, having killed his brother Pedro the Cruel, ended the civil wars in the kingdom of Léon and Castile. On Enrique's shield are the quartered arms of Léon, a black lion on a white ground, and Castile, a gold castle on a red ground. Source: Portrait of Enrique on a painting of the Virgin, 1367-79, Coll. of Don Ramon Vicente, Saragossa, Spain.

Portuguese Infantry, c. 1385

Previously organized along Muslim lines, the Portuguese army was reconstructed in the 1380's after the English pattern. This man wears mail and leans upon a pole-axe. Sources: 'Guards at the Tomb,' on 14th century effigy of Christ, Museu de Machado de Castro, Coimbra; 'Pilate's Soldiers,' c. 1390, Reliquary of Piedra, Historical Academy of Madrid.

Castilian Slinger, c. 1372

Castilian troops were effective in naval warfare. This man uses a staff-sling which could throw incendiary grenades against enemy ships. Sources: Bascinet and fresco, late 14th century, Prov. Museum, Burgos and Museo de Navarra, Pamplona.

Dom João I, king of Portugal,
c. 1385

João I was one of England's best friends and, aided by an English force, he defeated the Castilians at Alju-barrota in 1385. Here he wears light Iberian armour with a visored helmet. His shield bears the royal arms of Portugal, with a 'border of Castile.' Sources: Statue of a mounted knight and effigy of Ramon Berenguer II, both late 14th century, Ferreiros Chapel, Oliveira do Hospital, Portugal; and Gerona Cathedral, Spain.

Bellerophon Books

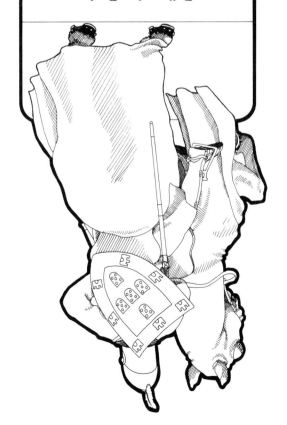

Moorish Horseman,
c. 1385

The Muslim kingdom of Granada in the south of Spain was tributary to Léon and Castile during the 14th century. It sent contingents to help the Castilians in various wars. The Moors wore little armour, but fought as light cavalry with long spears and leather *adarga* shields. Their costumes were often of very rich fabric. Source: Painted ceiling in Sala de Justicia, c. 1390, Alhambra, Granada.

Bellerophon Books

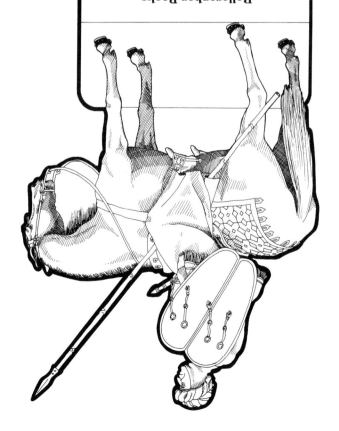

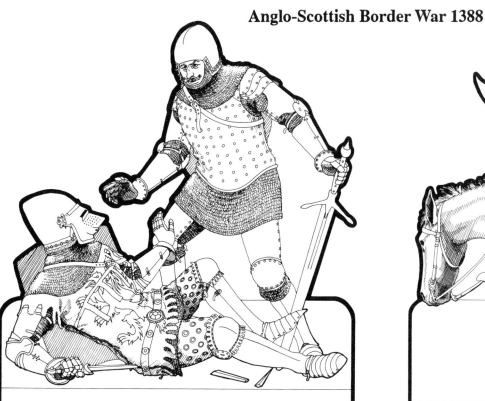

Henry Percy captured by the Lord Montgomery, 1388

Henry Percy, nick-named Hotspur, was twice defeated by an invading Scottish army in 1388. On the second occasion, at the battle of Otterburn, the young Hotspur was captured by Lord Montgomery of Eglintoun. Here Hotspur bears one of the Percy family arms, a blue lion on a gold ground, with his own cadency mark of a red bar. Lord Montgomery wields a typically Scottish heavy hand-and-a-half sword. His coat-of-arms was almost identical to that of the French monarchy, three gold fleurs-de-lys on a blue ground. Sources: (Hotspur) Effigy of Thomas, Earl of Warwick, St. Mary's Church, Warwick; painted retable, Norwich Cathedral; carved misericord, Worcester Cathedral, all late 14th century.

Bellerophon Books

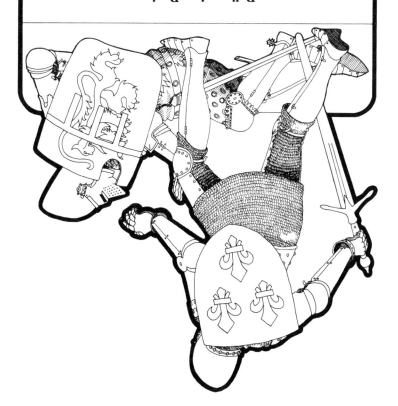

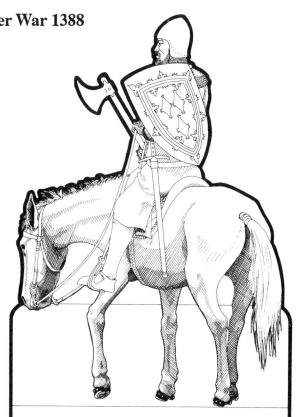

John, Earl of Moray, c. 1388

The Earl of Moray, with his force of Highlanders, was one of the leaders of a Scottish invasion that ravaged northern England in 1388. Here he wears typical Highland gear suitable for fighting on foot. The Earl of Moray's unusual coat-of-arms consisted of three red cushions surrounded by a red 'double tressure flory-counter-flory' on a silver ground. Sources: Carved warrior on the Cross of Reginaldus of Islay, late 14th century, National Museum of Antiquities, Edinburgh, Scotland; effigy of Bricius MacKinnon, 1350-1375, Iona Museum, Scotland.

Bellerophon Books

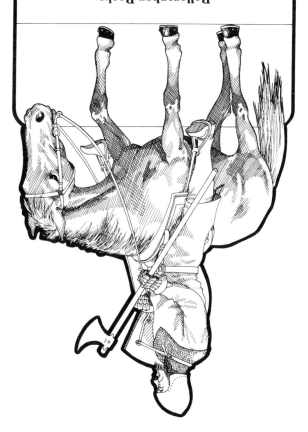

French in Italy 1391

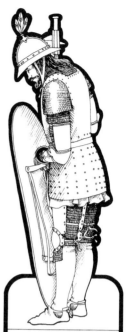

The Sire de Coucy, c. 1395

The French baron Enguerrand de Coucy was involved in both wars and diplomatic missions. In the 1390s, he led a campaign in Italy. Coucy's coat-of-arms consisted of blue and white crenellations between red stripes, quartered with the red and white arms of Austria. Sources: 'January' in *Très Riches Heures*, late 14th century, Musée Condé, Chantilly; seal of Enguerrand de Coucy, Bureaux des sceaux, National Archives, Paris; late 14th century bascinet, Musée d'Artillerie, Paris.

Bellerophon Books

Louis II of Anjou, c. 1395

Louis was claimant to the throne of Naples. His arms were almost the same as those of France. Sources: Relief of Count Tiberto VI Brandolini, c. 1397, S. Francesco, Bagnacavallo; 'Way to Calvary,' fresco, S. Gimignano, Italy.

Bellerophon Books

Genoese hand-gunner, c. 1390

This man holds a primitive example of a handgun. His mantlet-shield bears the arms of Genoa. Sources: Silver altar by Ser Giovanni, 1371, Cathedral, Pistoia; 'Battle of Clavigo,' fresco, c. 1370, Oratorio di S. Giorgio, Padua, Italy.

Bellerophon Books

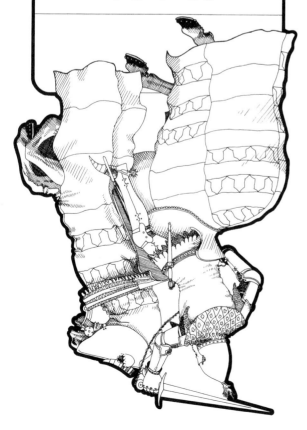

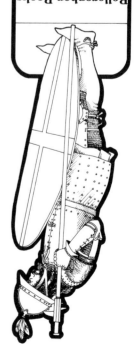

Welsh Rising 1400-1412

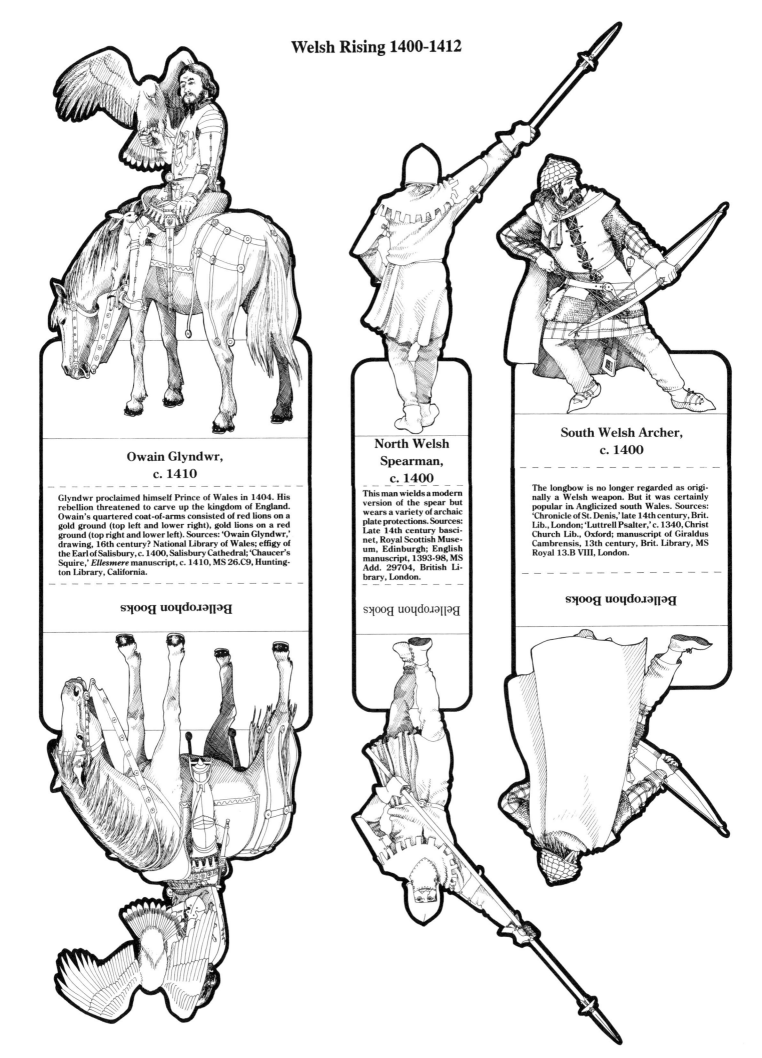

Owain Glyndwr, c. 1410

Glyndwr proclaimed himself Prince of Wales in 1404. His rebellion threatened to carve up the kingdom of England. Owain's quartered coat-of-arms consisted of red lions on a gold ground (top left and lower right), gold lions on a red ground (top right and lower left). Sources: 'Owain Glyndwr,' drawing, 16th century? National Library of Wales; effigy of the Earl of Salisbury, c. 1400, Salisbury Cathedral; 'Chaucer's Squire,' *Ellesmere* manuscript, c. 1410, MS 26.C9, Huntington Library, California.

North Welsh Spearman, c. 1400

This man wields a modern version of the spear but wears a variety of archaic plate protections. Sources: Late 14th century bascinet, Royal Scottish Museum, Edinburgh; English manuscript, 1393-98, MS Add. 29704, British Library, London.

South Welsh Archer, c. 1400

The longbow is no longer regarded as originally a Welsh weapon. But it was certainly popular in Anglicized south Wales. Sources: 'Chronicle of St. Denis,' late 14th century, Brit. Lib., London; 'Luttrell Psalter,' c. 1340, Christ Church Lib., Oxford; manuscript of Giraldus Cambrensis, 13th century, Brit. Library, MS Royal 13.B VIII, London.

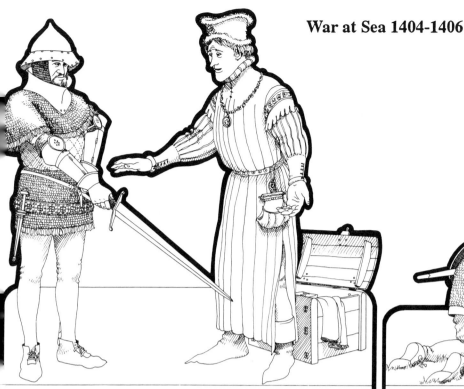

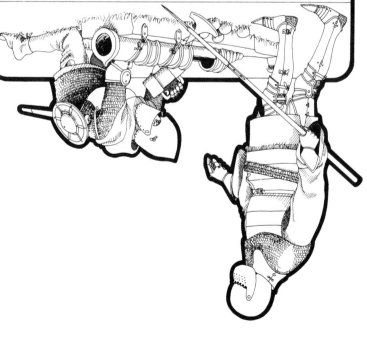

Don Pedro Niño,
Count of Buelna,
c. 1405

As the most successful Castilian galley captain of his day, Don Pedro preyed upon English shipping in the Atlantic and Channel as an ally of France. Here he wears an early form of *cabacete* and *barbote* to protect head and throat, plus light armour suitable for marine warfare. Sources: 'Retablo of San Jorge,' Valencia, c. 1415, Victoria and Albert Museum; effigy of Don Bernardo de Anglesolo, c. 1390, Aragon; St. George, c. 1420, Tarragona.

English Merchant
c. 1410

The 100 Years War had surprisingly little effect on English trade, except when England lost control of the seas as it did at the start of the 15th century. This merchant wears the heavy rich fabrics and jewelry fashionable in the reign of Henry IV. Sources: Miniature of Lord Lovell and John Siferwas, c. 1405, Brit. Lib., MS Harl 7026, London; 'Chaucer reading,' Corpus Christi College, Cambridge Library.

French gunner,
c. 1408

This man is working with a breech-loading siege-cannon. His helmet is a crudely modified bascinet and he wears a breastplate held by straps across his back. Sources: North Italian manuscript, early 15th century, MS 348, Wallace Coll., London; late 14th century bascinet, Bardini Coll., Florence; 'Betrayal,' French manuscript, late 14th century, Parement de Narbonne, Louvre.

The Seigneur de Rambures,
c. 1405

This young French knight rose to become the French king's master of crossbows at the battle of Agincourt. He carries a pole-axe. His coat-of-arms consisted of three gold bars across a red ground. Sources: 'Chronicle d' Angleterre,' c. 1400, Bib. Nat., Paris; 'Crucifixion and St. George,' painting from Chartreuse de Champmol, c. 1410, Louvre.

Bellerophon Books

Bellerophon Books

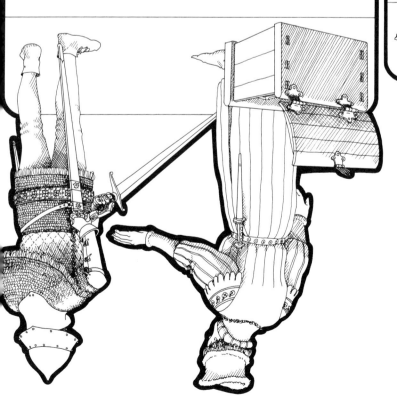

French Civil War 1404-1412

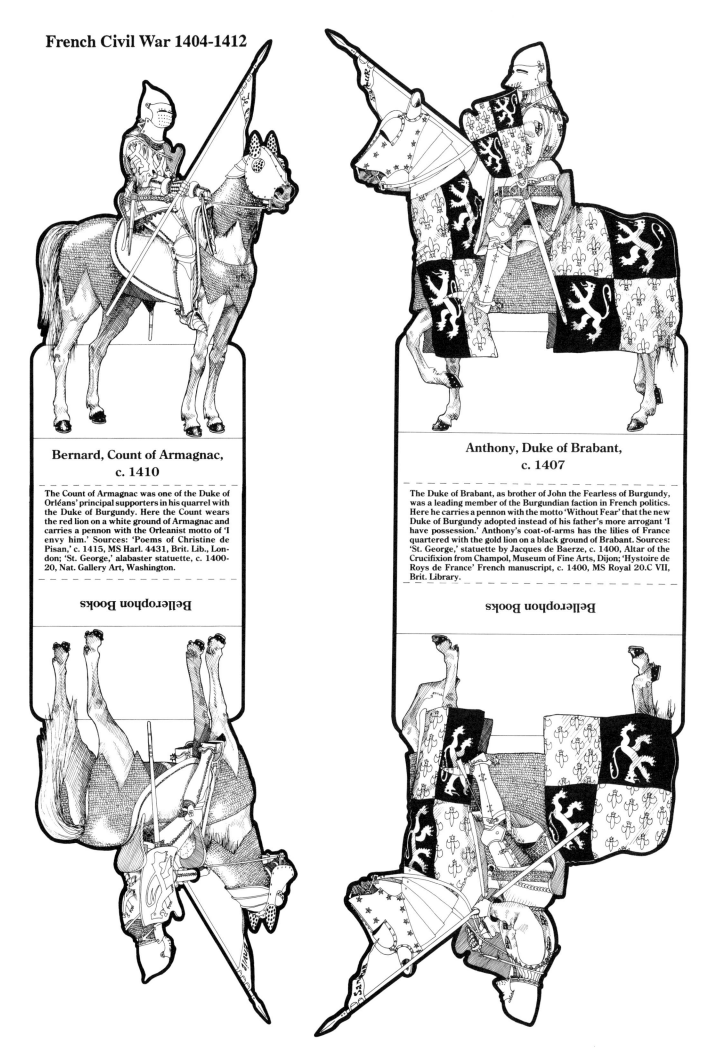

Bernard, Count of Armagnac, c. 1410

The Count of Armagnac was one of the Duke of Orléans' principal supporters in his quarrel with the Duke of Burgundy. Here the Count wears the red lion on a white ground of Armagnac and carries a pennon with the Orleanist motto of 'I envy him.' Sources: 'Poems of Christine de Pisan,' c. 1415, MS Harl. 4431, Brit. Lib., London; 'St. George,' alabaster statuette, c. 1400-20, Nat. Gallery Art, Washington.

Bellerophon Books

Anthony, Duke of Brabant, c. 1407

The Duke of Brabant, as brother of John the Fearless of Burgundy, was a leading member of the Burgundian faction in French politics. Here he carries a pennon with the motto 'Without Fear' that the new Duke of Burgundy adopted instead of his father's more arrogant 'I have possession.' Anthony's coat-of-arms has the lilies of France quartered with the gold lion on a black ground of Brabant. Sources: 'St. George,' statuette by Jacques de Baerze, c. 1400, Altar of the Crucifixion from Champol, Museum of Fine Arts, Dijon; 'Hystoire de Roys de France' French manuscript, c. 1400, MS Royal 20.C VII, Brit. Library.

Bellerophon Books

Agincourt Campaign 1415

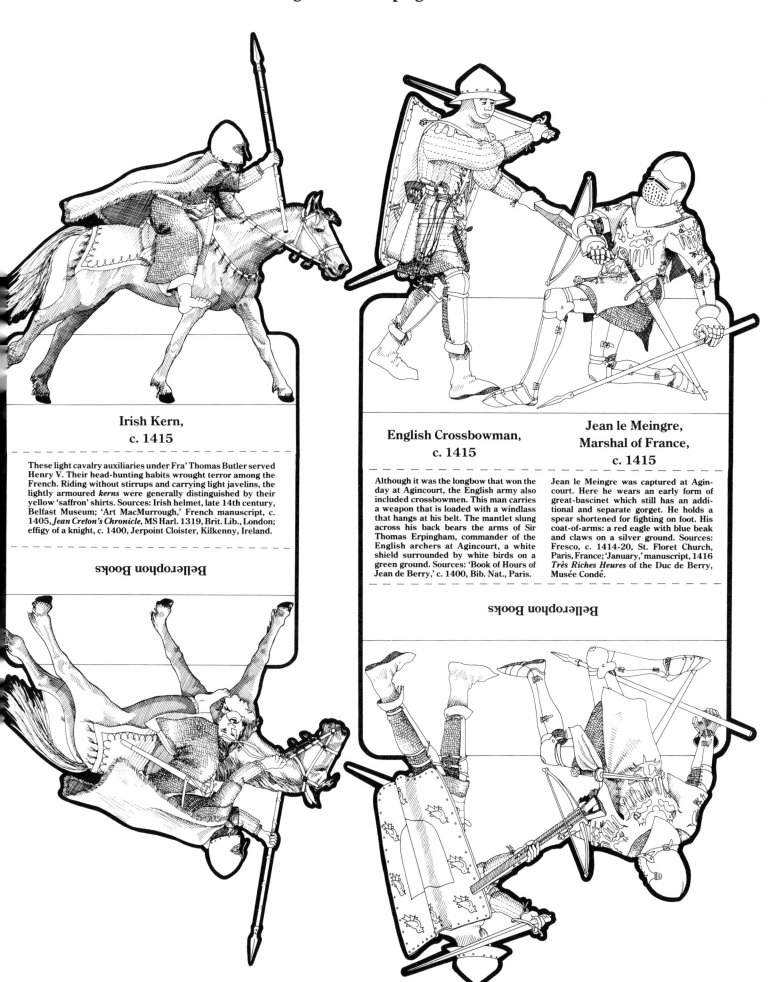

Irish Kern,
c. 1415

These light cavalry auxiliaries under Fra' Thomas Butler served Henry V. Their head-hunting habits wrought terror among the French. Riding without stirrups and carrying light javelins, the lightly armoured *kerns* were generally distinguished by their yellow 'saffron' shirts. Sources: Irish helmet, late 14th century, Belfast Museum; 'Art MacMurrough,' French manuscript, c. 1405, *Jean Creton's Chronicle*, MS Harl. 1319, Brit. Lib., London; effigy of a knight, c. 1400, Jerpoint Cloister, Kilkenny, Ireland.

Bellerophon Books

English Crossbowman,
c. 1415

Although it was the longbow that won the day at Agincourt, the English army also included crossbowmen. This man carries a weapon that is loaded with a windlass that hangs at his belt. The mantlet slung across his back bears the arms of Sir Thomas Erpingham, commander of the English archers at Agincourt, a white shield surrounded by white birds on a green ground. Sources: 'Book of Hours of Jean de Berry,' c. 1400, Bib. Nat., Paris.

Jean le Meingre,
Marshal of France,
c. 1415

Jean le Meingre was captured at Agincourt. Here he wears an early form of great-bascinet which still has an additional and separate gorget. He holds a spear shortened for fighting on foot. His coat-of-arms: a red eagle with blue beak and claws on a silver ground. Sources: Fresco, c. 1414-20, St. Floret Church, Paris, France; 'January,' manuscript, 1416 *Très Riches Heures* of the Duc de Berry, Musée Condé.

Bellerophon Books

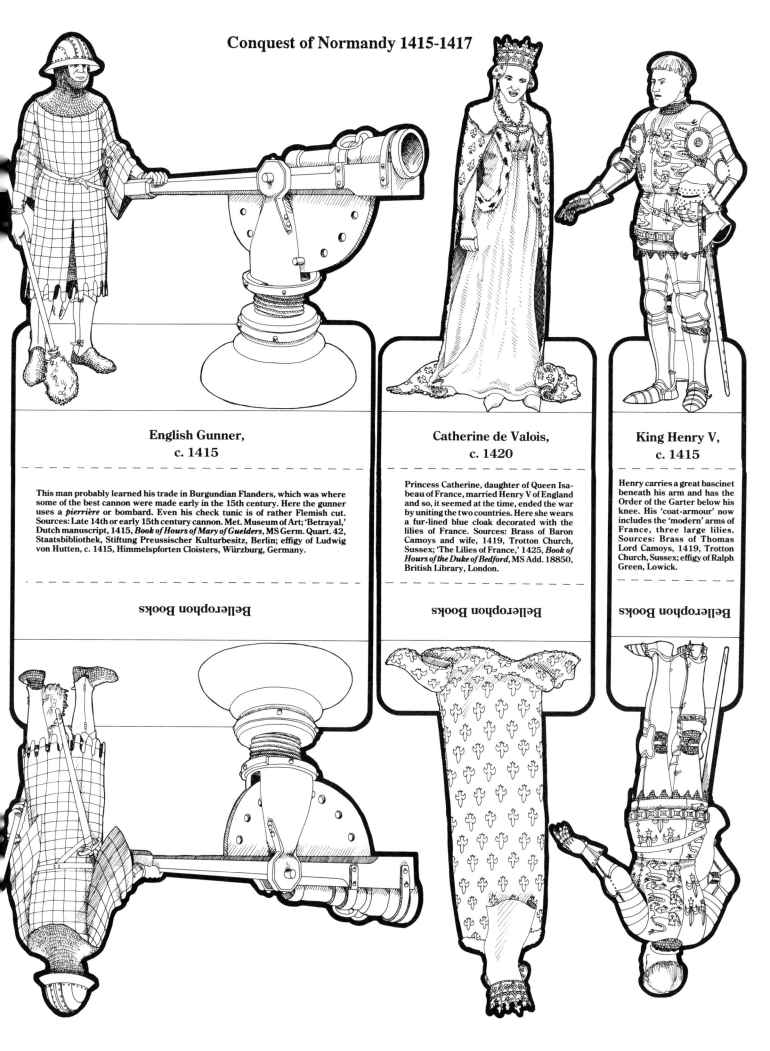

English Gunner, c. 1415

This man probably learned his trade in Burgundian Flanders, which was where some of the best cannon were made early in the 15th century. Here the gunner uses a *pierrière* or bombard. Even his check tunic is of rather Flemish cut. Sources: Late 14th or early 15th century cannon. Met. Museum of Art; 'Betrayal,' Dutch manuscript, 1415, *Book of Hours of Mary of Guelders*, MS Germ. Quart. 42, Staatsbibliothek, Stiftung Preussischer Kulturbesitz, Berlin; effigy of Ludwig von Hutten, c. 1415, Himmelspforten Cloisters, Würzburg, Germany.

Bellerophon Books

Catherine de Valois, c. 1420

Princess Catherine, daughter of Queen Isabeau of France, married Henry V of England and so, it seemed at the time, ended the war by uniting the two countries. Here she wears a fur-lined blue cloak decorated with the lilies of France. Sources: Brass of Baron Camoys and wife, 1419, Trotton Church, Sussex; 'The Lilies of France,' 1425, *Book of Hours of the Duke of Bedford*, MS Add. 18850, British Library, London.

Bellerophon Books

King Henry V, c. 1415

Henry carries a great bascinet beneath his arm and has the Order of the Garter below his knee. His 'coat-armour' now includes the 'modern' arms of France, three large lilies. Sources: Brass of Thomas Lord Camoys, 1419, Trotton Church, Sussex; effigy of Ralph Green, Lowick.

Bellerophon Books

The Anglo-Burgundian Alliance 1421-1424

The Dauphin Charles, c. 1421

Charles was called the 'Dauphin' even after he was crowned as king. His clothes are decorated with the badge of a crowned and winged stag. Sources: Portrait of Charles VII by Fouquet, Louvre; tapestry made for Charles VII, c. 1430, Metropolitan Museum of Art.

Bellerophon Books

Italian Mercenary, c. 1425

The Dauphin Charles enlisted foreign mercenaries. This man wears a sallet and a jerkin. Sources: Painted chests, early 15th century, National Gallery, Dublin; Victoria and Albert Museum, London.

Bellerophon Books

Seigneur de l'Isle-Adam, 1418

His coat-of-arms is a white-sleeved arm on a divided ground of blue over yellow. Source: Effigy of Ludwig von Hutten, c. 1315, Himmelspforten Cloisters, Würzburg, Germany.

Bellerophon Books

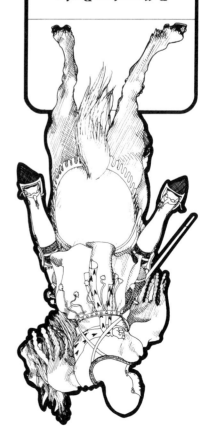

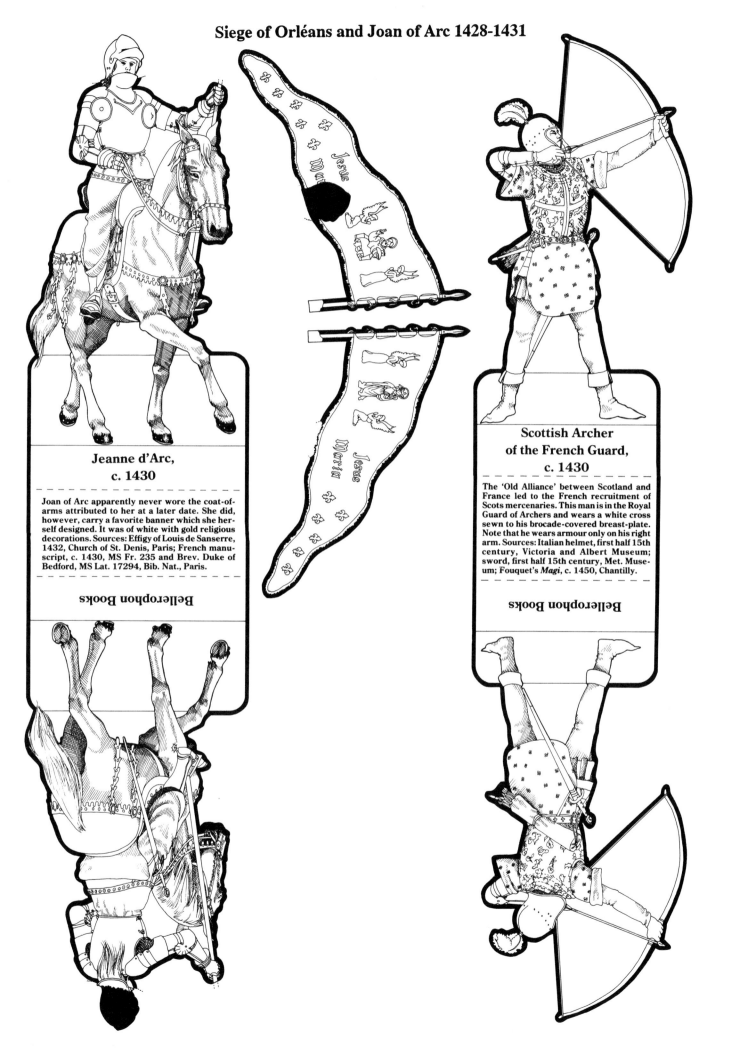

Siege of Orléans and Joan of Arc 1428-1431

Jeanne d'Arc,
c. 1430

Joan of Arc apparently never wore the coat-of-arms attributed to her at a later date. She did, however, carry a favorite banner which she herself designed. It was of white with gold religious decorations. Sources: Effigy of Louis de Sanserre, 1432, Church of St. Denis, Paris; French manuscript, c. 1430, MS Fr. 235 and Brev. Duke of Bedford, MS Lat. 17294, Bib. Nat., Paris.

Bellerophon Books

Scottish Archer
of the French Guard,
c. 1430

The 'Old Alliance' between Scotland and France led to the French recruitment of Scots mercenaries. This man is in the Royal Guard of Archers and wears a white cross sewn to his brocade-covered breast-plate. Note that he wears armour only on his right arm. Sources: Italian helmet, first half 15th century, Victoria and Albert Museum; sword, first half 15th century, Met. Museum; Fouquet's *Magi*, c. 1450, Chantilly.

Bellerophon Books

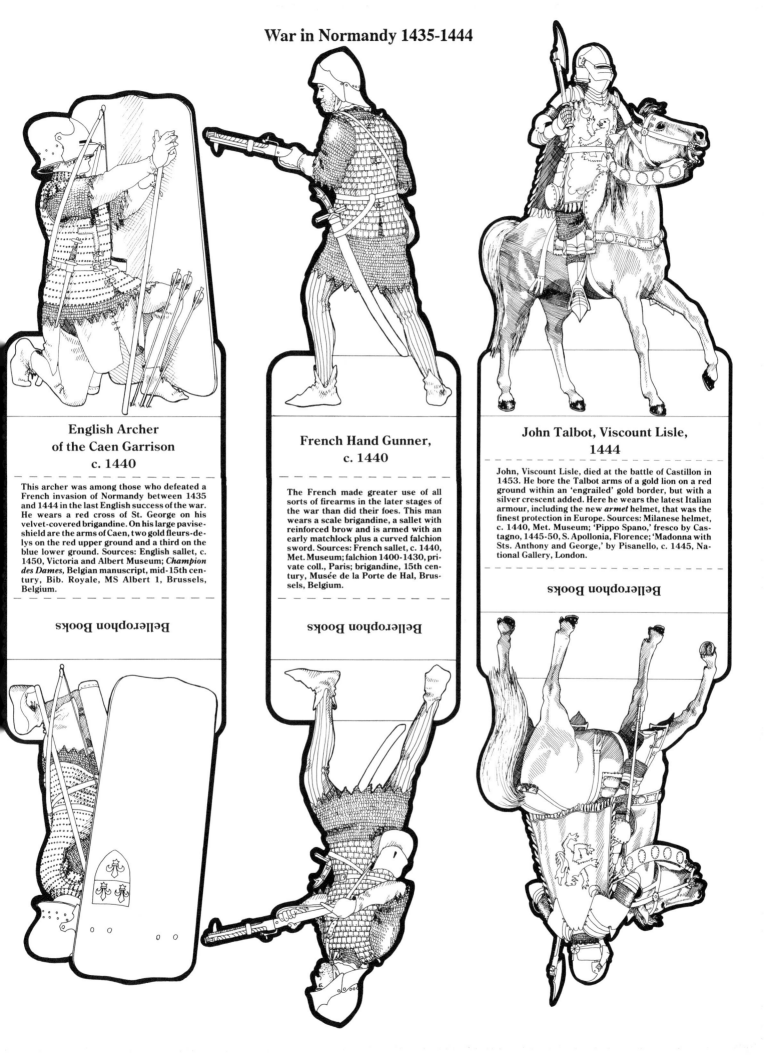

English Archer
of the Caen Garrison
c. 1440

This archer was among those who defeated a French invasion of Normandy between 1435 and 1444 in the last English success of the war. He wears a red cross of St. George on his velvet-covered brigandine. On his large pavise-shield are the arms of Caen, two gold fleurs-de-lys on the red upper ground and a third on the blue lower ground. Sources: English sallet, c. 1450, Victoria and Albert Museum; *Champion des Dames*, Belgian manuscript, mid-15th century, Bib. Royale, MS Albert 1, Brussels, Belgium.

Bellerophon Books

French Hand Gunner,
c. 1440

The French made greater use of all sorts of firearms in the later stages of the war than did their foes. This man wears a scale brigandine, a sallet with reinforced brow and is armed with an early matchlock plus a curved falchion sword. Sources: French sallet, c. 1440, Met. Museum; falchion 1400-1430, private coll., Paris; brigandine, 15th century, Musée de la Porte de Hal, Brussels, Belgium.

Bellerophon Books

John Talbot, Viscount Lisle,
1444

John, Viscount Lisle, died at the battle of Castillon in 1453. He bore the Talbot arms of a gold lion on a red ground within an 'engrailed' gold border, but with a silver crescent added. Here he wears the latest Italian armour, including the new *armet* helmet, that was the finest protection in Europe. Sources: Milanese helmet, c. 1440, Met. Museum; 'Pippo Spano,' fresco by Castagno, 1445-50, S. Apollonia, Florence; 'Madonna with Sts. Anthony and George,' by Pisanello, c. 1445, National Gallery, London.

Bellerophon Books

The English Defeat 1449-1453

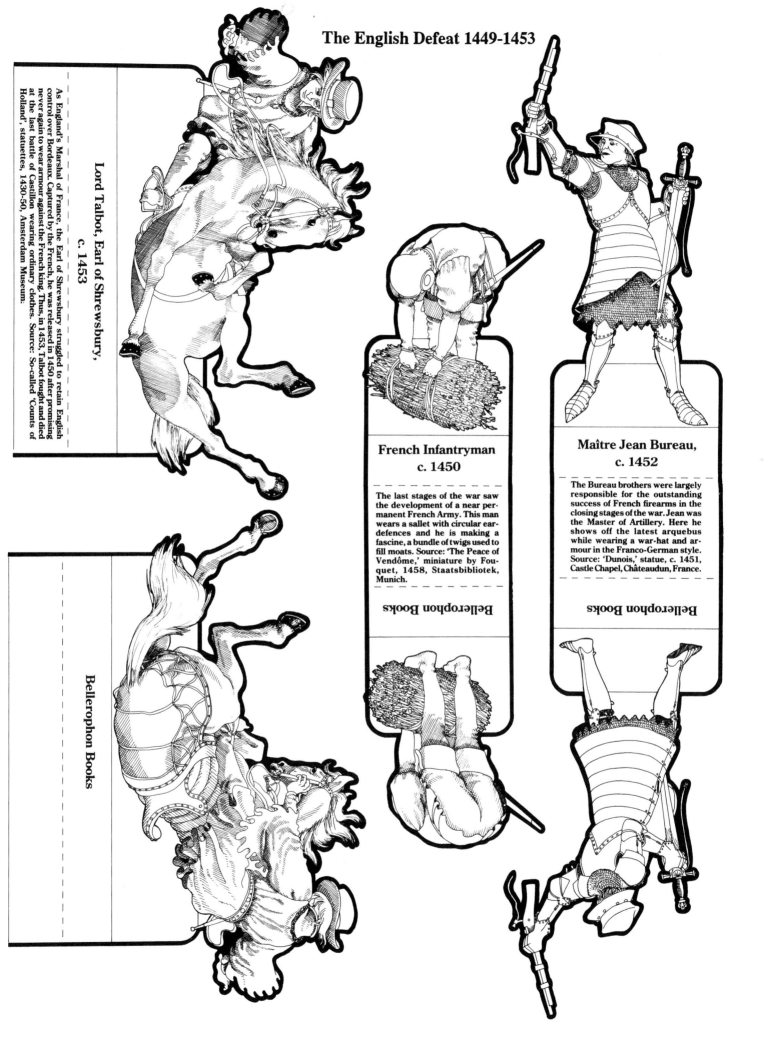

Lord Talbot, Earl of Shrewsbury, c. 1453

As England's Marshal of France, the Earl of Shrewsbury struggled to retain English control over Bordeaux. Captured by the French, he was released in 1450 after promising never again to wear armour against the French king. Thus, in 1453, Talbot fought and died at the last battle of Castillon wearing ordinary clothes. Source: So-called 'Counts of Holland', statuettes, 1430-50, Amsterdam Museum.

French Infantryman c. 1450

The last stages of the war saw the development of a near permanent French Army. This man wears a sallet with circular ear-defences and he is making a fascine, a bundle of twigs used to fill moats. Source: 'The Peace of Vendôme,' miniature by Fouquet, 1458, Staatsbibliotek, Munich.

Bellerophon Books

Maître Jean Bureau, c. 1452

The Bureau brothers were largely responsible for the outstanding success of French firearms in the closing stages of the war. Jean was the Master of Artillery. Here he shows off the latest arquebus while wearing a war-hat and armour in the Franco-German style. Source: 'Dunois,' statue, c. 1451, Castle Chapel, Châteaudun, France.

Bellerophon Books

Bellerophon Books